THE VICTORIA AND ALBERT MUSEUM
Christmas List Book

RANDOM CENTURY

LONDON SYDNEY AUCKLAND JOHANNESBURG

FIRST PUBLISHED IN 1989 BY
CENTURY BENHAM LTD
A DIVISION OF RANDOM CENTURY LTD
20 VAUXHALL BRIDGE ROAD
LONDON SW1V 2SA

REPRINTED 1990

SET IN COPPERPLATE GOTHIC
BY FMT GRAPHICS LIMITED
SOUTHWARK LONDON
PRINTED AND BOUND IN SINGAPORE

PICTURE RESEARCH BY RACHEL MARY BARNES
EDITORIAL RESEARCH BY JANE ROSS
DESIGNED BY POLLY DAWES

ISBN 0712625291

COVER ILLUSTRATION FROM A VICTORIAN CHRISTMAS CARD

Contents

CHRISTMAS CARDS

FAMILY CHRISTMAS CARDS

Name _____

Address _____

_____

Year _____

Name _____

Address _____

_____

Year _____

Name _____

Address _____

_____

Year _____

Name _____

Address _____

_____

Year _____

Name _____

Address _____

_____

Year _____

Name _____

Address _____

_____

Year _____

Name _____

Address _____

_____

Year _____

IN THE BLEAK MID-WINTER
FROSTY WIND MADE MOAN,
EARTH STOOD HARD AS IRON,
WATER LIKE A STONE;
SNOW HAD FALLEN, SNOW ON SNOW,
SNOW ON SNOW,
IN THE BLEAK MID-WINTER
LONG AGO.

CHRISTINA ROSSETTI

Name _____

Address _____

_____

Year _____

Name _____
Address _____
_____
Year _____

Name _____
Address _____
_____
Year _____

Name _____
Address _____
_____
Year _____

Name _____
Address _____
_____
Year _____

Name _____
Address _____
_____
Year _____

A HAPPY
NEW YEAR TO YOU

Name _____
Address _____
_____
Year _____

Name _____
Address _____
_____
Year _____

FAMILY CHRISTMAS CARDS

Name _____
Address _____
_____
_____

Year _____

Name _____
Address _____
_____
_____

Year _____

Name _____
Address _____
_____
_____

Year _____

Name _____
Address _____
_____
_____

Year _____

Name _____
Address _____
_____
_____

Year _____

Name _____
Address _____
_____
_____

Year _____

Christmas chimes.
In the still air
The moon swims fair,
The joyous bells are ringing loud and sweet,
With urgent voice
They cry "rejoice
Christians! come forth your new-born Lord to meet!"

Name _____
Address _____
_____
_____

Year _____

Name _____
Address _____
_____
_____

Year _____

Name _____
Address _____
_____
_____

Year _____

Name _____
Address _____
_____
_____

Year _____

Name _____
Address _____
_____
_____

Year _____

Name _____
Address _____
_____
_____

Year _____

I HEARD THE BELLS ON CHRISTMAS DAY
THEIR OLD FAMILIAR CAROLS PLAY,
AND WILD AND SWEET
THE WORDS REPEAT,
OF 'PEACE ON EARTH, GOOD WILL TO MEN!'
HENRY WADSWORTH LONGFELLOW

Name _____
Address _____
_____
_____

Year _____

Name _____
Address _____
_____
_____

Year _____

Name _____
Address _____
_____
_____

Year _____

Name _____
Address _____
_____
_____
Year _____

Name _____
Address _____
_____
_____
Year _____

Name _____
Address _____
_____
_____
Year _____

Name _____
Address _____
_____
_____
Year _____

Christmas Greeting.
To thee may Christmas come
Rich with the whole year's
harvest-home.

Name _____
Address _____
_____
_____
Year _____

Name _____
Address _____
_____
_____
Year _____

Name _____

Address _____

_____

_____

Year _____

Name _____

Address _____

_____

_____

Year _____

Name _____

Address _____

_____

_____

Year _____

Name _____

Address _____

_____

Year _____

Name _____

Address _____

_____

_____

Year _____

Name _____

Address _____

_____

_____

Year _____

Name _____

Address _____

_____

Year _____

OH, YES, WELL DO I REMEMBER
YOUR JOYFUL VOICE AND HEARTFELT GLEE;
ACCEPT, THEN, IN THIS BLEAK DECEMBER,
A MERRY CHRISTMAS, DEAR, FROM ME.

VICTORIAN CHRISTMAS CARD VERSE

Name _____

Address _____

_____

_____

Year _____

FAMILY CHRISTMAS CARDS

Name _____
Address _____
_____
_____

Year _____

Name _____
Address _____
_____
_____

Year _____

Name _____
Address _____
_____

Year _____

Name _____
Address _____
_____
_____

Year _____

SILENT NIGHT, HOLY NIGHT.
ALL IS CALM, ALL IS BRIGHT.
ROUND YON VIRGIN MOTHER AND CHILD,
HOLY INFANT SO TENDER AND MILD,
SLEEP IN HEAVENLY PEACE,
SLEEP IN HEAVENLY PEACE.

CAROL

Name _____
Address _____
_____
_____

Year _____

Name _____
Address _____
_____
_____

Year _____

Name _____
Address _____
_____
_____

Year _____

Name _____
Address _____
_____
_____

Year _____

Name _____
Address _____
_____
_____

Year _____

Name _____
Address _____
_____
_____

Year _____

Name _____
Address _____
_____
_____

Year _____

Name _____
Address _____
_____
_____

Year _____

Name _____
Address _____
_____
_____

Year _____

Name _____
Address _____
_____
_____

Year _____

FAMILY CHRISTMAS CARDS

Name _____

Address _____

_____

Year _____

Name _____

Address _____

_____

Year _____

Name _____

Address _____

_____

Year _____

Name _____

Address _____

_____

Year _____

Name _____

Address _____

_____

Year _____

Name _____

Address _____

_____

Year _____

Name _____

Address _____

_____

Year _____

Name _____

Address _____

_____

Year _____

GOD BLESS THE MASTER OF THIS HOUSE,
THE MISTRESS ALSO,
AND ALL THE LITTLE CHILDREN
THAT ROUND THE TABLE GO;
AND ALL YOUR KIN AND KINSFOLK,
THAT DWELL BOTH FAR AND NEAR:
I WISH YOU A MERRY CHRISTMAS
AND A HAPPY NEW YEAR.

ANON

Name _____

Address _____

_____

Year _____

Name _____

Address _____

_____

Year _____

Name _____

Address _____

_____

Year _____

Name _____

Address _____

_____

Year _____

Name _____

Address _____

_____

Year _____

FRIENDS' CHRISTMAS CARDS

Name _____
Address _____
_____
_____

Year _____

Name _____
Address _____
_____
_____

Year _____

Name _____
Address _____
_____
_____

Year _____

Name _____
Address _____
_____
_____

Year _____

Name _____
Address _____
_____
_____

Year _____

SOME SAY THAT EVER 'GAINST THAT SEASON COMES
WHEREIN OUR SAVIOUR'S BIRTH IS CELEBRATED,
THE BIRD OF DAWNING SINGETH ALL NIGHT LONG;
AND THEN, THEY SAY, NO SPIRIT CAN WALK ABROAD
WILLIAM SHAKESPEARE, HAMLET

Name _____
Address _____
_____
_____

Year _____

Name _____
Address _____
_____
_____

Year _____

All Christmas joys be yours.

Name _____
Address _____
_____
_____

Year _____

Name _____
Address _____
_____
_____

Year _____

Name _____
Address _____
_____
_____

Year _____

Name _____
Address _____
_____
_____

Year _____

Name _____
Address _____
_____
_____

Year _____

Name _____
Address _____
_____
_____

Year _____

Name _____
Address _____
_____
_____

Year _____

FRIENDS' CHRISTMAS CARDS

A HAPPY NEW YEAR.

With the glad New Year we come,
    From the forest's leafless bowers,
When the moss of many hues
    Decks the ruined crumbling towers,
Clustered berries meet the eye
    Midst the shining leaves of green,
Now in winter brightly glow
    Like the coral's ruddy sheen.

(COPYRIGHT)   J. L. WATSON.

Name _____
Address _____
_____
_____
Year _____

Name _____
Address _____
_____
_____
Year _____

Name _____
Address _____
_____
_____
Year _____

Name _____
Address _____
_____
_____
Year _____

Name _____   Name _____
Address _____   Address _____
_____   _____
_____   _____

Year _____   Year _____

Name _____   Name _____
Address _____   Address _____
_____   _____

Year _____   Year _____

Name _____   Name _____
Address _____   Address _____
_____   _____

Year _____   Year _____

Name _____   Name _____
Address _____   Address _____
_____

Year _____   Year _____

WE WISH YOU A MERRY CHRISTMAS.
WE WISH YOU A MERRY CHRISTMAS.
WE WISH YOU A MERRY CHRISTMAS
AND A HAPPY NEW YEAR.
GOOD TIDINGS WE BRING
FOR YOU AND YOUR KIN.
WE WISH YOU A MERRY CHRISTMAS
AND A HAPPY NEW YEAR.
CAROL

FRIENDS' CHRISTMAS CARDS

Name _____
Address _____
_____
_____

Year _____

Name _____
Address _____
_____

Year _____

Name _____
Address _____
_____

Year _____

Name _____
Address _____
_____

Year _____

Name _____
Address _____
_____

Year _____

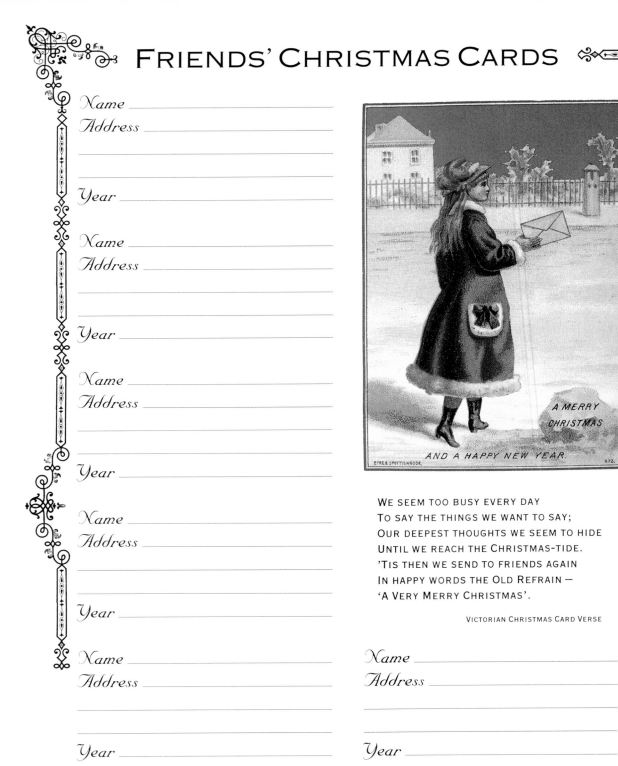

A MERRY CHRISTMAS AND A HAPPY NEW YEAR.

WE SEEM TOO BUSY EVERY DAY
TO SAY THE THINGS WE WANT TO SAY;
OUR DEEPEST THOUGHTS WE SEEM TO HIDE
UNTIL WE REACH THE CHRISTMAS-TIDE.
'TIS THEN WE SEND TO FRIENDS AGAIN
IN HAPPY WORDS THE OLD REFRAIN —
'A VERY MERRY CHRISTMAS'.

VICTORIAN CHRISTMAS CARD VERSE

Name _____
Address _____
_____
_____

Year _____

Name _____
Address _____
_____
_____
Year _____

Name _____
Address _____
_____
_____
Year _____

Name _____
Address _____
_____
_____
Year _____

Name _____
Address _____
_____
_____
Year _____

Name _____
Address _____
_____
_____
Year _____

Name _____
Address _____
_____
_____
Year _____

Name _____
Address _____
_____
_____
Year _____

Name _____
Address _____
_____
_____
Year _____

WISHING YOU A   HAPPY NEW YEAR

Friends' Christmas Cards

Name _____

Address _____

_____

_____

Year _____

Name _____

Address _____

_____

_____

Year _____

Name _____

Address _____

_____

_____

Year _____

Name _____

Address _____

_____

_____

Year _____

Name _____

Address _____

_____

_____

Year _____

It has created quite a new trade, and has opened up a new field of labour for artists, lithographers, engravers, printers, ink and pasteboard makers . . . All the year round brains are at work devising new designs and inventing novelties. The very cheap Christmas cards come from Germany where they can be produced at a much cheaper rate, but all the more artistic and more highly finished cards are the result of English workmanship.

From The Times, 1883

Name _____

Address _____

_____

_____

Year _____

Name _____

Address _____

_____

_____

Year _____

Name _____

Address _____

_____

_____

Year _____

Name _____

Address _____

_____

_____

Year _____

Name _____

Address _____

_____

_____

Year _____

Name _____

Address _____

_____

Year _____

Name _____

Address _____

_____

_____

Year _____

Name _____

Address _____

_____

_____

Year _____

A VERY MERRY X-MAS

Name _____

Address _____

_____

Year _____

BUSINESS CHRISTMAS CARDS

Name _____
Address _____
_____
_____
Year _____

Name _____
Address _____
_____
_____
Year _____

Name _____
Address _____
_____
_____
Year _____

Name _____
Address _____
_____
_____
Year _____

Name _____
Address _____
_____
_____
Year _____

Name _____
Address _____
_____
_____
Year _____

Name _____
Address _____
_____
_____
Year _____

LISTEN! IN THE FROSTY DAWN
FROM HIS LEAFLESS BOUGH
THE SAME BRAVE SONG HE EVER SANG
A ROBIN'S SINGING NOW.

ROBIN'S SONG BY RODNEY BENNETT

Name _____
Address _____
_____
_____
Year _____

Name _____

Address _____

_____

_____

Year _____

Name _____

Address _____

_____

_____

Year _____

Name _____

Address _____

_____

_____

Year _____

Name _____

Address _____

_____

_____

Year _____

BUSINESS CHRISTMAS CARDS

Name _____
Address _____
_____

Year _____

Name _____
Address _____
_____

Year _____

Name _____
Address _____
_____

Year _____

Name _____
Address _____
_____

Year _____

Name _____
Address _____
_____

Year _____

Name _____
Address _____
_____

Year _____

Name _____
Address _____
_____

Year _____

Name _____
Address _____
_____

Year _____

JINGLE BELLS, JINGLE BELLS,
JINGLE ALL THE WAY;
OH! WHAT JOY IT IS TO RIDE
IN A ONE-HORSE OPEN SLEIGH.
JINGLE BELLS, JINGLE BELLS,
JINGLE ALL THE WAY.
OH! WHAT JOY IT IS TO RIDE
IN A ONE-HORSE OPEN SLEIGH.
CAROL

Name _____ Name _____
Address _____ Address _____
_____ _____

Year _____ Year _____

Name _____ Name _____
Address _____ Address _____
_____ _____

Year _____ Year _____

Name _____ Name _____
Address _____ Address _____
_____ _____

Year _____ Year _____

Business Christmas Cards ❄

Name _____   Name _____
Address _____   Address _____
_____   _____
_____   _____

Year _____   Year _____

Name _____   Name _____
Address _____   Address _____
_____   _____
_____   _____

Year _____   Year _____

WISHING YOU THE COMPLIMENTS OF THE SEASON

Name _____

Address _____

_____

_____

Year _____

> WHAT SWEETER MUSIC CAN WE BRING
> THAN A CAROL FOR TO SING
> THE BIRTH OF THIS OUR HEAV'NLY KING
> AWAKE THE VOICE! AWAKE THE STRING:
> DARK AND DULL NIGHT FLY HENCE AWAY,
> AND GIVE THE HONOUR OF THIS DAY,
> THAT SEES DECEMBER TURNED TO MAY . . .
>
> CAROL, BY ROBERT HERRICK

Name _____

Address _____

_____

_____

Year _____

Name _____

Address _____

_____

_____

Year _____

Name _____

Address _____

_____

_____

Year _____

Name _____

Address _____

_____

_____

Year _____

Name _____

Address _____

_____

_____

Year _____

Name _____

Address _____

_____

_____

Year _____

BUSINESS CHRISTMAS CARDS

Name _____
Address _____
_____
_____

Year _____

Name _____
Address _____
_____
_____

Year _____

Name _____
Address _____
_____
_____

Year _____

Name _____
Address _____
_____
_____

Year _____

Name _____
Address _____
_____
_____

Year _____

Name _____
Address _____
_____
_____

Year _____

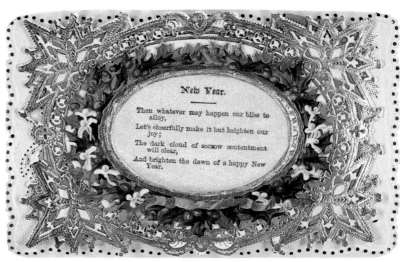

New Year.

Then whatever may happen our bliss to
alloy,
Let's cheerfully make it but heighten our
joy;
The dark cloud of sorrow contentment
will clear,
And brighten the dawn of a happy New
Year.

CHRISTMAS PRESENTS

FAMILY PRESENTS

Name _____

Given _____

Received _____

Year _____

Name _____

Given _____

Received _____

Year _____

Name _____

Given _____

Received _____

Year _____

Name _____

Given _____

Received _____

Year _____

Name _____

Given _____

Received _____

Year _____

Name _____

Given _____

Received _____

Year _____

Name _____

Given _____

Received _____

Year _____

Name _____

Given _____

Received _____

Year _____

Name _____

Given _____

Received _____

Year _____

> WHAT, FATHER CHRISTMAS! HERE AGAIN?
> WITH YULE LOG ON YOUR BACK
> AND MIGHTY STORE OF RACY THINGS
> WELL STUFFED WITHIN YOUR PACK.
>
> CHRISTMAS VERSE, 1848

Name _____

Given _____

Received _____

Year _____

Name _____

Given _____

Received _____

Year _____

Name _____

Given _____

Received _____

Year _____

Name _____

Given _____

Received _____

Year _____

Name _____

Given _____

Received _____

Year _____

Name _____

Given _____

Received _____

Year _____

Name _____

Given _____

Received _____

Year _____

Name _____

Given _____

Received _____

Year _____

Name _____

Given _____

Received _____

Year _____

Name _____

Given _____

Received _____

Year _____

FAMILY PRESENTS

Name _____
Given _____
Received _____
Year _____

Name _____
Given _____
Received _____
Year _____

Name _____
Given _____
Received _____
Year _____

Name _____
Given _____
Received _____
Year _____

Name _____
Given _____
Received _____
Year _____

Name _____
Given _____
Received _____
Year _____

Name _____
Given _____
Received _____
Year _____

Name _____
Given _____
Received _____
Year _____

Name _____
Given _____
Received _____
Year _____

The last sound she heard was the ringing of the
bells that ushered in the Christmas morn; and,
with their bright echoes in her heart, she
wandered away into the land of dreams with
her fairy doll of the Christmas-tree.

'Plessy's Christmas Eve',
Little Folks Magazine, 1877

Name _____
Given _____
Received _____
Year _____

Name _____
Given _____
Received _____
Year _____

Name _____
Given _____
Received _____
Year _____

Name _____
Given _____
Received _____
Year _____

Name _____
Given _____
Received _____
Year _____

Name _____
Given _____
Received _____
Year _____

Name _____
Given _____
Received _____
Year _____

Name _____
Given _____
Received _____
Year _____

FAMILY PRESENTS

Name _____
Given _____
Received _____
Year _____

Name _____
Given _____
Received _____
Year _____

Name _____
Given _____
Received _____
Year _____

Name _____
Given _____
Received _____
Year _____

Name _____
Given _____
Received _____
Year _____

Name _____
Given _____
Received _____
Year _____

Name _____
Given _____
Received _____
Year _____

Name _____
Given _____
Received _____
Year _____

Name _____

Given _____

Received _____

Year _____

Name _____

Given _____

Received _____

Year _____

Name _____

Given _____

Received _____

Year _____

Name _____

Given _____

Received _____

Year _____

Name _____

Given _____

Received _____

Year _____

Name _____

Given _____

Received _____

Year _____

Name _____

Given _____

Received _____

Year _____

'TWAS MISTLETOE MORNING,
AND CHANTICLEER'S WARNING
HAD SUMMONED FINE FOLKS FROM
THEIR BEDS AND THEIR BLANKETS:
WHEN I SAW IN A VISION
OF DREAMLAND ELYSIAN,
A BEVY OF CUPIDS SWARM FORTH
FOR THEIR PRANKETS.
THERE WAS FUN IN THEIR FACES,
AS ALL TOOK THEIR PLACES,
AND LINK'D THEMSELVES LAUGHINGLY —
MAD LITTLE FROLICKERS;
AND NEVER SUCH LAUGHTER
SHOOK ROOF, BEAM, AND RAFTER,
AS SHOOK THE FAT SIDES OF
THESE ROYSTERING ROLICKERS.

WITH UNFETTERED ACTIONS
THEY FORMED IN TWO FACTIONS,
AND, NUDE AS OLD STATUES,
SELECTED THEIR PLACES;
LITTLE ROSY CAROUSERS,
WITHOUT ANY TROUSERS,
AND QUITE INDEPENDENT OF
STRAPS AND OF BRACES.
SUCH TINTS WERE THEIR LIMBS ON,
SUCH HUES OF RICH CRIMSON,
SUCH ROSES, AND LILIES,
WAX APPLES, AND CHERRIES,
THAT THEY GLEAMED HOT AND SUNNY,
AS, WITH FROLICKINGS FUNNY,
THEY SNOWBALLED EACH OTHER
WITH MISTLETOE BERRIES!

'MISTLETOE MORNING'
BY CUTHBERT BEDE, 1855

FAMILY PRESENTS

Name _____
Given _____
Received _____
Year _____

Name _____
Given _____
Received _____
Year _____

Name _____
Given _____
Received _____
Year _____

Name _____
Given _____
Received _____
Year _____

Name _____
Given _____
Received _____
Year _____

Name _____
Given _____
Received _____
Year _____

Name _____
Given _____
Received _____
Year _____

Name _____
Given _____
Received _____
Year _____

Name _____
Given _____
Received _____
Year _____

> CHRISTMAS COMES! WHILE YOU ARE SLEEPING,
> IN THE HOLY ANGEL'S KEEPING,
> HE AROUND YOUR BED IS CREEPING,
> AND WITHIN THE CURTAINS PEEPING,
> LEAVING FOR ALL GOOD GIRLS AND BOYS
> SUCH MERRY GAMES AND PRETTY TOYS.
> VICTORIAN CHRISTMAS CARD VERSE

Name _____
Given _____
Received _____
Year _____

Name _____
Given _____
Received _____
Year _____

Name ——————————————————
Given ——————————————————
Received ——————————————————
Year ——————————————————

Name ——————————————————
Given ——————————————————
Received ——————————————————
Year ——————————————————

Name ——————————————————
Given ——————————————————
Received ——————————————————
Year ——————————————————

Name ——————————————————
Given ——————————————————
Received ——————————————————
Year ——————————————————

FRIENDS' PRESENTS

Name _____
Given _____
Received _____
Year _____

Name _____
Given _____
Received _____
Year _____

Name _____
Given _____
Received _____
Year _____

Name _____
Given _____
Received _____
Year _____

Name _____
Given _____
Received _____
Year _____

Name _____
Given _____
Received _____
Year _____

Name _____
Given _____
Received _____
Year _____

Name _____
Given _____
Received _____
Year _____

Name _____
Given _____
Received _____
Year _____

Name _____
Given _____
Received _____
Year _____

Name _____
Given _____
Received _____
Year _____

Name _____
Given _____
Received _____
Year _____

Name _____
Given _____
Received _____
Year _____

Name _____
Given _____
Received _____
Year _____

Name _____
Given _____
Received _____
Year _____

Name _____
Given _____
Received _____
Year _____

Name _____
Given _____
Received _____
Year _____

Compliments of the season.

ON THE TWELFTH DAY OF CHRISTMAS
MY TRUE LOVE SENT TO ME
TWELVE LORDS A-LEAPING,
ELEVEN LADIES DANCING,
TEN PIPERS PIPING,
NINE DRUMMERS DRUMMING,
EIGHT MAIDS A-MILKING,
SEVEN SWANS A-SWIMMING,
SIX GEESE A-LAYING,
FIVE GOLD RINGS,
FOUR COLLY BIRDS,
THREE FRENCH HENS,
TWO TURTLE-DOVES
AND A PARTRIDGE IN A PEAR-TREE.

CHRISTMAS CAROL

FRIENDS' PRESENTS

Name _____
Given _____
Received _____
Year _____

Name _____
Given _____
Received _____
Year _____

Name _____
Given _____
Received _____
Year _____

Name _____
Given _____
Received _____
Year _____

Name _____
Given _____
Received _____
Year _____

Name _____
Given _____
Received _____
Year _____

Name _____
Given _____
Received _____
Year _____

Name _____
Given _____
Received _____
Year _____

Name _____
Given _____
Received _____
Year _____

Name _____
Given _____
Received _____
Year _____

Name _____
Given _____
Received _____
Year _____

Name _____
Given _____
Received _____
Year _____

Name _____
Given _____
Received _____
Year _____

Name _____
Given _____
Received _____
Year _____

Name _____
Given _____
Received _____
Year _____

Name _____
Given _____
Received _____
Year _____

Name _____
Given _____
Received _____
Year _____

Name _____
Given _____
Received _____
Year _____

Name _____
Given _____
Received _____
Year _____

'TWAS THE NIGHT BEFORE CHRISTMAS,
WHEN ALL THROUGH THE HOUSE
NOT A CREATURE WAS STIRRING, NOT EVEN A MOUSE;
THE STOCKINGS WERE HUNG BY THE CHIMNEY WITH CARE,
IN HOPES THAT ST NICHOLAS SOON WOULD BE THERE. . .

CLEMENT CLARK MOORE, A VISIT FROM ST NICHOLAS

FRIENDS' PRESENTS

Name _____
Given _____
Received _____
Year _____

Name _____
Given _____
Received _____
Year _____

Name _____
Given _____
Received _____
Year _____

Name _____
Given _____
Received _____
Year _____

Name _____
Given _____
Received _____
Year _____

The Queen desires to live, as far as the cares of
State permit, the life of a private lady. Her
Majesty loves the seclusion of this lordly
estate, and here at Christmas time she enjoys
the society of her children and grandchildren,
who meet together as less exalted families do at
this merry season to reciprocate the same
homely delights as those which are
experienced throughout the land.

W. F. Dawson about Queen Victoria

Name _____
Given _____
Received _____
Year _____

Name _____
Given _____
Received _____
Year _____

Name _____
Given _____
Received _____
Year _____

Name _____
Given _____
Received _____
Year _____

Name _____
Given _____
Received _____
Year _____

Name _____
Given _____
Received _____
Year _____

Name _____
Given _____
Received _____
Year _____

Name _____
Given _____
Received _____
Year _____

Name _____
Given _____
Received _____
Year _____

Name _____
Given _____
Received _____
Year _____

Name _____
Given _____
Received _____
Year _____

Name _____
Given _____
Received _____
Year _____

Name _____
Given _____
Received _____
Year _____

Business Presents

Name _____
Given _____
Received _____
Year _____

Name _____
Given _____
Received _____
Year _____

Name _____
Given _____
Received _____
Year _____

Name _____
Given _____
Received _____
Year _____

Name _____
Given _____
Received _____
Year _____

Name _____
Given _____
Received _____
Year _____

Name _____
Given _____
Received _____
Year _____

Name _____
Given _____
Received _____
Year _____

Name _____
Given _____
Received _____
Year _____

Name _____
Given _____
Received _____
Year _____

What can I give Him,
Poor as I am?
If I were a shepherd
I would bring a lamb;
If I were a wise man
I would do my part;
Yet what I can I give Him,
Give my heart.

From In the Bleak Mid-Winter, Christina Rossetti

Name _____
Given _____
Received _____
Year _____

Name _____
Given _____
Received _____
Year _____

Name _____
Given _____
Received _____
Year _____

Name _____   Name _____
Given _____   Given _____
Received _____   Received _____
Year _____   Year _____

Name _____   Name _____
Given _____   Given _____
Received _____   Received _____
Year _____   Year _____

Name _____   Name _____
Given _____   Given _____
Received _____   Received _____
Year _____   Year _____

Name _____   Name _____
Given _____   Given _____
Received _____   Received _____
Year _____   Year _____

BUSINESS PRESENTS

Name _____
Given _____
Received _____
Year _____

Name _____
Given _____
Received _____
Year _____

Name _____
Given _____
Received _____
Year _____

Name _____
Given _____
Received _____
Year _____

Name _____
Given _____
Received _____
Year _____

Name _____
Given _____
Received _____
Year _____

Name _____
Given _____
Received _____
Year _____

Name _____
Given _____
Received _____
Year _____

Name _____
Given _____
Received _____
Year _____

A suitable present for a man is lavender water,
twenty years old, double distilled and sold in
quaint old English bottles. It is a recognised
fact that the one scent a man is not ashamed to
use is lavender.

From *The Lady's Realm* (late Victorian)

ACCEPT THIS SOUVENIR
of my best wishes for a very happy Christmas

Name _____
Given _____
Received _____
Year _____

Name _____
Given _____
Received _____
Year _____

Name _____
Given _____
Received _____
Year _____

Name _____
Given _____
Received _____
Year _____

Name _____
Given _____
Received _____
Year _____

Name _____
Given _____
Received _____
Year _____

Name _____
Given _____
Received _____
Year _____

Name _____
Given _____
Received _____
Year _____

BUSINESS PRESENTS

Name _____
Given _____
Received _____
Year _____

Name _____
Given _____
Received _____
Year _____

Name _____
Given _____
Received _____
Year _____

Name _____
Given _____
Received _____
Year _____

Name _____
Given _____
Received _____
Year _____

Name _____
Given _____
Received _____
Year _____

Name _____
Given _____
Received _____
Year _____

Name _____
Given _____
Received _____
Year _____

Name _____
Given _____
Received _____
Year _____

May your Christmas happy be

By the 1880s turkey had replaced goose as the popular main dish at Christmas. Mince pies began to appear in Royal Christmas Menus early in Victoria's reign.
A tradition when making Christmas pudding was for each member of the family to stir the ingredients from East to West in recognition of The Three Kings.

CHRISTMAS DAY MENUS

V.A.M.

CHRISTMAS PARTIES

A MERRY CHRISTMAS
AND
A HAPPY NEW YEAR
.TO YOU

PROVERBS

'Proverbs' is a capital old game. When it is played, one member of the company leaves the room, and the rest fix upon a well-known proverb. The banished guest returns and asks each person a question, who in reply is bound to bring in one word of the proverb in its proper order, and the questioner tries to find out from these answers what the proverb is. A very amusing variety of this game is called 'shooting proverbs'. The guests each appropriate one word of the proverb as before. The one who is trying to guess the proverb comes in, steps into the middle of the room, and calls out in a commanding voice, 'Make ready! Present! Fire!' At the word 'Fire!', all the company shout their own words at once, and the proverb is to be guessed from the sound, which is a very confusing one.

From 'Christmas Games for Everybody' by Phillis Browne in *Cassell's Family Magazine*

Q. **Why is Prince Albert liable to a military flogging from Queen Victoria?**

A. **Because he is subject to her!**

A Christmas Card riddle, 1840s

PARTIES FOR ADULTS

SNAP DRAGON

There are some games that seem to belong
peculiarly to Christmas, and foremost
amongst these is the game of 'Snap Dragon'.

Here he comes with flaming bowl,
Don't he mean to take his toll,
Snip! Snap! Dragon!
Take care you don't take too much,
Be not greedy in your clutch,
Snip! Snap! Dragon!

With his blue and lapping tongue,
Many of you will be stung,
Snip! Snap! Dragon!
For he snaps at all that comes,
Snatching at his feast of plums,
Snip! Snap! Dragon!

When this pastime is decided upon, a number
of raisins are put into a large, broad, shallow
bowl, and a little brandy or other spirit is
poured over the fruit. The lights in the room
are then extinguished, the spirit is ignited, and
the bystanders in turn plunge their hands
through the flames and endeavour to obtain
possession of the fruit. This, of course, is not
easily done; it requires both nerve and agility,
and the unavailing attempts of the company
cause a good deal of fun. Added to this, the
burning spirit gives a lurid glare which lights
up the eager faces of the guests, and has quite a
weird-like effect.
From 'Christmas Games for Everybody', *Cassell's
Family Magazine*

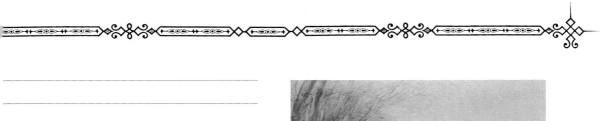

PARTIES FOR CHILDREN

A very peculiar sensation may be experienced by those who endeavour to blow out a candle without seeing where it is. The candle is lighted and placed upon a table. The player is then blindfolded, and is told to walk three steps to the right, to the left, backwards, and forwards; and in each case to come back to his first position. He is then to turn round twice, and blow out the candle. In nine cases out of ten he will blow quite away from the place where the candle stands.

From 'Christmas Games for Everybody' by Phillis Browne
in *Cassell's Family Magazine*

THINK UPON THE GIRLS AND BOYS
WHO GET NO PRETTY CHRISTMAS TOYS,
WHO SUFFER WANT, AND COLD, AND CARE,
AND HELP THEM, BOTH BY ALMS AND PRAYER.

VICTORIAN CHRISTMAS CARD VERSE

PARTIES FOR CHILDREN

A grave sergeant-at-law, or the elderly author of an incomparable and incomprehensible treatise upon metaphysics, or a spectacled physician of sixty sitting on his hams on a carpet, and passing the slipper under them with all the dexterity, if not with all the glee, of a school boy, is a sight to be enjoyed.

'Hunt the Slipper', from 'Uncle Tom' (Victorian writer) in the *Illustrated London News*

SHADOW BUFF

'Shadow Buff' is a pretty variety of 'Blind Man's Buff', and it is a safe, quiet, and pretty game for young people. If there is a white curtain in the room, it should be fastened down to make a smooth surface. If there is no curtain, a sheet or a tablecloth will be required. The one who is to be blind man seats himself before the curtain with his back to his companions, and to the light. The rest pass behind him so that their shadows may be thrown upon the white surface, and the one who he names from the shadow is to take the place of blind man. The players are allowed to dress themselves up, and disguise themselves in any way they like. Very confusing shadows may be made with a little ingenuity. The hair may be let down, or fastened up in a style different to that in which it is usually worn; or the player may wrap himself in a sheet and spread his arms wide under it, thus making a shadow like a bat; or the finger may be held over the nose to hide its shape. If the blind man looks round at the actors he must pay a forfeit for the offence.

From 'Christmas Games for Everybody', *Cassell's Family Magazine*

DUMB CRAMBO

When playing 'Dumb Crambo' half the party leave the room, and those who remain choose a verb, which the others are to guess. When the absent ones return, they are told of a word which will rhyme with the word fixed upon, and they then consult together to find out what it is. Instead of speaking their guess, they act it. If they guess rightly, they are applauded; if they fail, they are hissed. A word spoken on either side, excepting by the actors for the purpose of private consultation, entails a forfeit.

From 'Christmas Games for Everybody' by Phillis Browne
in *Cassell's Family Magazine*

CHRISTMAS SHOPPING LIST

FOOD

OLD ENGLISH CHRISTMAS by H S MARKS ARA 2

"The Turkeys, Madam, you see here, are tender, plump, and far from dear."

OLD CHRISTMAS IS COME
FOR TO KEEP OPEN HOUSE;
HE SCORNS TO BE GUILTY
OF STARVING A MOUSE:
THEN COME, BOYS, AND WELCOME,
FOR DIET THE CHIEF,
PLUM-PUDDING, GOOSE, CAPON,
MINC'D PIES, AND ROAST BEEF.

RESTORATION BALLAD

DRINK

DRINK NOW THE STRONG BEER,
CUT THE WHITE LOAF HERE,
THE WHILE THE MEAT IS SHREDDING;
FOR THE RARE MINCE-PIE
AND THE PLUMS STAND BY
TO FILL THE PASTE THAT'S A-KNEADING.

ROBERT HERRICK

PRESENTS

A mighty magician has touched London with his wand. The spirit of altruism has descended upon the city of self. The note of preparation for the great festival of the Christian Church, which was sounded early in November when the windows of the stationers, the booksellers' shops, and the railway stalls became suddenly gay with the coloured plates of Christmas numbers innumerable, has increased in volume as time went on. Now, on the eve of the great day, there is not a street in the capital containing a shop, from its broadest thoroughfare to its narrowest by-way, that has not decked its windows for the Christmas market.

George R. Sims

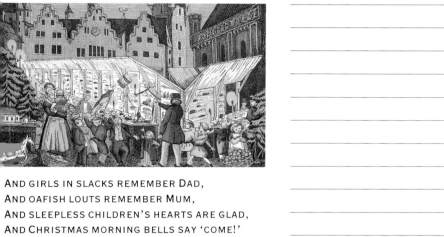

AND GIRLS IN SLACKS REMEMBER DAD,
AND OAFISH LOUTS REMEMBER MUM,
AND SLEEPLESS CHILDREN'S HEARTS ARE GLAD,
AND CHRISTMAS MORNING BELLS SAY 'COME!'
EVEN TO SHINING ONES WHO DWELL
SAFE IN THE DORCHESTER HOTEL.
AND IS IT TRUE? AND IS IT TRUE,
THIS MOST TREMENDOUS TALE OF ALL,
SEEN IN A STAINED-GLASS WINDOW'S HUE,
A BABY IN AN OX'S STALL?

CHRISTMAS, JOHN BETJEMAN

PRESENTS

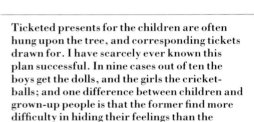

Ticketed presents for the children are often hung upon the tree, and corresponding tickets drawn for. I have scarcely ever known this plan successful. In nine cases out of ten the boys get the dolls, and the girls the cricket-balls; and one difference between children and grown-up people is that the former find more difficulty in hiding their feelings than the latter.

'How to Give a Children's Party' from (Victorian) *Cassell's Family Magazine*

OH! WE'VE ALL BEEN SHOPPING,
SHOP, SHOP, SHOPPING,
WE'VE VISITED THE LOWTHER
AND THE BURLINGTON ARCADE
AND WE'RE ALL OF US A-DROPPING,
DROP, DROP, DROPPING
FAST ASLEEP, EXCEPT PAPA,
THAT IDLE MAN, WHO ONLY PAID.

CAPTION TO DRAWING, 1876

DECORATIONS

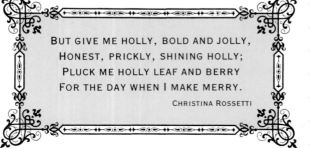

BUT GIVE ME HOLLY, BOLD AND JOLLY,
HONEST, PRICKLY, SHINING HOLLY;
PLUCK ME HOLLY LEAF AND BERRY
FOR THE DAY WHEN I MAKE MERRY.

CHRISTINA ROSSETTI

Miscellaneous

CHRISTMAS ACCOUNTS

FOOD

Item	Cost	Item	Cost

Item	Cost	Item	Cost

DRINK

Item	Cost	Item	Cost

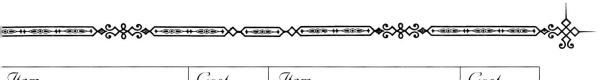

Item	Cost	Item	Cost

 # PRESENTS

Item	Cost	Item	Cost

HOLIDAY PLANNER

DECEMBER 19 . . .

24
Christmas Eve

25
Christmas Day

26
Boxing Day

27

28

29

30

31
New Year's Eve

1 **JANUARY 19 . . .**
New Year's Day

24
Christmas Eve

DECEMBER 19...

25
Christmas Day

26
Boxing Day

27

28

29

30

31
New Year's Eve

1
New Year's Day

JANUARY 19...

 # HOLIDAY PLANNER

24 *Christmas Eve*

DECEMBER 19...

25 *Christmas Day*

26 *Boxing Day*

27

28

29

30

31 *New Year's Eve*

1 *New Year's Day*

JANUARY 19...

24 *Christmas Eve*	DECEMBER 19 . . .
25 *Christmas Day*	
26 *Boxing Day*	
27	
28	
29	
30	
31 *New Year's Eve*	
1 *New Year's Day*	JANUARY 19 . . .

CINDERELLA

HOLIDAY PLANNER

24 *Christmas Eve*	DECEMBER 19 . . .
25 *Christmas Day*	
26 *Boxing Day*	
27	
28	
29	
30	
31 *New Year's Eve*	
1 *New Year's Day*	JANUARY 19 . . .

THANK YOU LETTERS

ADULTS

Name _____
Gift _____
Date Sent _____

Name _____
Gift _____
Date Sent _____

Name _____
Gift _____
Date Sent _____

Name _____
Gift _____
Date Sent _____

Name _____
Gift _____
Date Sent _____

Name _____
Gift _____
Date Sent _____

Name _____
Gift _____
Date Sent _____

Name _____
Gift _____
Date Sent _____

Name _____
Gift _____
Date Sent _____

Name _____
Gift _____
Date Sent _____

Name _____
Gift _____
Date Sent _____

Name _____
Gift _____
Date Sent _____

Name _____
Gift _____
Date Sent _____

> AT CHRISTMAS BE MERRY,
> AND THANKFUL WITHAL,
> AND FEAST YOUR POOR NEIGHBOURS,
> THE GREAT WITH THE SMALL.
> THOMAS TUSSER